WHAT'S THE POINT OF THIS BOOK?

I hope you enjoy working through this book. It took months of development and years of playing with ideas before that. **If you like it, please tell your friends and write a review on Amazon!** We are a family business: customer recommendations make an enormous difference.

This series grew out of my more exam-oriented resources in 11 Plus Lifeline. So many parents got in touch to ask for further writing materials, sometimes for exam preparation and sometimes just because their children enjoyed being creative, that I decided to to do something about it. I wanted the resources to be about more than exams, and I wanted them to be suitable for people all across the English-speaking world.

RSL Creative Writing focuses on descriptive writing and short stories, but the series also includes packs covering letters, emails and persuasive essays. There are even opportunities to continue a story by a famous author, blending your style with theirs.

The guiding idea behind this series is that a young person's creativity deserves respect. Far too often, children are taught to write childishly, with a focus on shortcuts: *use lots of adjectives, add these ten "wow words"*, and so on. However, I've found that many children can write as well as adults, if only they are shown how. By teaching them cheats rather than encouraging them to think about language in a mature way, grown-ups do them no favours.

Children should be shown the power of words. They should be taught that language is an enormous toolbox, full of possibilities but requiring careful judgment. The challenge we face is to choose words effectively, finding the best ways to shape our readers' thoughts and feelings.

Learning to write well involves learning to read well. Everybody finds it difficult to spot weaknesses in their own writing. For this reason, if we want to see things from a reader's point of view, it's best to start by looking at somebody else's work. That's why this book is full of examples. Mind you, not all of them are *good* examples!

Confident children will be able to use these resources independently. However, the series is likely to be even more useful when parents and children discuss things together … especially if both of you attempt the exercises and compare your answers. Try it! You may be surprised by the results.

Happy writing!

Robert

ALSO AVAILABLE

RSL Creative Writing: further volumes

11 Plus Lifeline (printable resources for all 11+ subjects):
www.11pluslifeline.com

RSL 11+ Comprehension

RSL 11+ Comprehension: Volume 2

RSL 11+ Maths

RSL 8+ to 10+ Comprehension

RSL 13+ Comprehension

GCSE Maths by RSL

GCSE Spanish by RSL

GCSE French by RSL

GCSE German by RSL

RSL Creative Writing: Book 1
by Robert Lomax

Published by RSL Educational Ltd

Company 10793232
VAT 252515326
17 Woodside Road, Bricket Wood, St Albans
Registered in England & Wales

Design and typesetting by
Heather Macpherson at Raspberry Creative Type

Photographs on pages 2, 22, 24, 57 and 89 © iStockphoto.com.
All other images © Shutterstock.com.

www.rsleducational.co.uk

CONTENTS

WRITING POWERFUL DESCRIPTIONS

This pack will show you how to describe a scene really effectively in a short piece of writing.

SANDSTORM

This pack will show you how to describe a scene really effectively in a short piece of writing.

Effectively? This means that you need to take your reader with you into the place and the character that you're describing. For the few minutes that it takes somebody to read your work, they should be able to imagine that they are there.

THIS IMAGE SHOWS A DESERT SCENE, FAR FROM ANYWHERE, WITH A SOLITARY BOY RIDING A CAMEL. IT IS JUST BEFORE SUNSET AND A SANDSTORM IS BEGINNING.

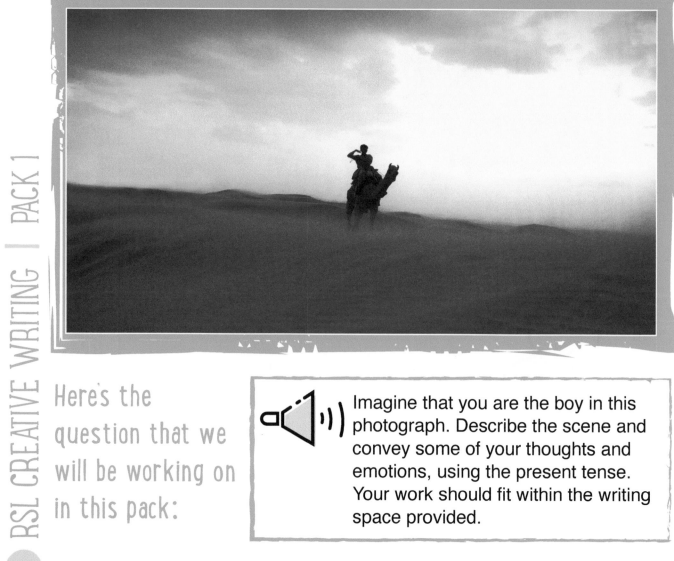

Here's the question that we will be working on in this pack:

Imagine that you are the boy in this photograph. Describe the scene and convey some of your thoughts and emotions, using the present tense. Your work should fit within the writing space provided.

USEFUL HINTS

Because this is the first pack, you may not have a clear idea of what to do. That's OK!

Here are some hints to get you started:

- Read the instructions carefully. You are writing as the boy in the photo, so you need to write about "**I**", not "**he**". You also need to use the present tense: "**I am**", not "**I was**". You should talk about the character's "**thoughts**", as well as his "**emotions**" (feelings).

- Everybody's personality is different. What is this person like? Is he determined, or cautious and prone to worry? Does he love his camel, or does it irritate him?

- There shouldn't be much plot: you're writing a description, not a story. However, a little bit of narrative development might help you to structure your writing. Does the sandstorm get stronger? Does the boy struggle up the side of a dune? Does the camel get excited, before being brought back under control? If you can come up with one simple idea of this sort, it will make your task easier and more enjoyable.

- Your job is to describe <u>this</u> scene. Don't give background ("**Atul is an orphan from Jodhpur. When he was five, his parents were killed in a railway accident, after which he was raised by his sisters. His uncle ...**") or jump forwards in time ("**Five hours later he reached the outskirts of a village**"). Focus on making a short period of time – at most, a few minutes – as interesting as possible.

- Bring the scene to life with sensory images, so that the reader can imagine being there. The usual list of five senses is **smell**, **sight**, **taste**, **touch** and **hearing**, but you don't need to use all of them all the time! Try not to always choose the most obvious sense. THERE WILL BE LOTS MORE ABOUT THE FIVE SENSES IN PACK 2.

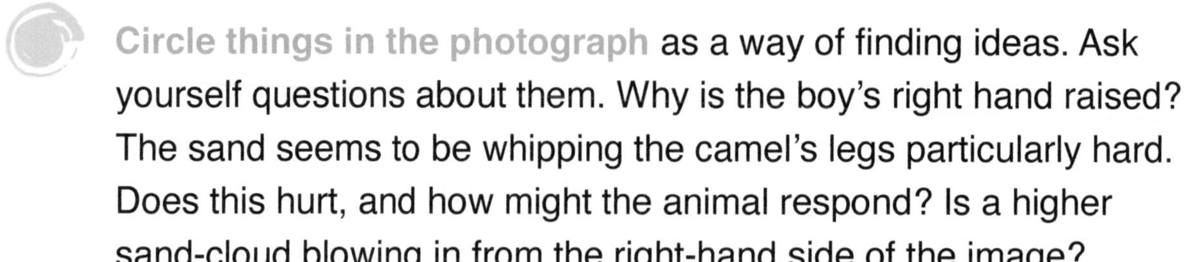

- **Circle things in the photograph** as a way of finding ideas. Ask yourself questions about them. Why is the boy's right hand raised? The sand seems to be whipping the camel's legs particularly hard. Does this hurt, and how might the animal respond? Is a higher sand-cloud blowing in from the right-hand side of the image?

- **Start a new paragraph when your writing shifts focus** – for example, from describing the dunes to talking about what the camel is doing. Short paragraphs are fine!

- **Plan each sentence in your head before you write it.** Look for simple, direct ways to communicate your ideas.

- **Check your writing.** Think about your most frequent mistakes – the things that drive your teachers mad – and look most carefully for these. Check your work against my hints (this list!) as well.

- **If there are things you'd like to change,** you can write a new version.

That's a lot to bear in mind! These are the most important things:

- focus on the picture
- do exactly what the question asks
- be as descriptive as possible

YOUR ANSWER

Now it's time to have a go, writing in the following answer space.

Imagine that you are the boy in this photograph. Describe the scene and convey some of your thoughts and emotions, using the present tense. Your work should fit within the writing space provided.

....

....

....

....

....

....

....

....

....

....

....

....

....

....

....

....

....

....

....

Well done!

You've just completed the first writing task in this course. There will almost certainly be things to improve, but you should feel proud of having created something original

- and perhaps also beautiful.

KATIE'S ANSWER

In order to write well, we have to learn how to read well.

It's always hard to recognise the strengths and weaknesses of your own writing: if you didn't think it was good, you wouldn't have written it that way! For this reason, the best way to make your own writing better is to practise improving somebody else's.

We're shortly going to look at Katie's answer. As you'll see, her work contains some excellent ideas, but there are plenty of things to be improved.

- What has Katie done that you could have done too?
- What did you do that Katie could have done?
- Can you circle the mistakes?

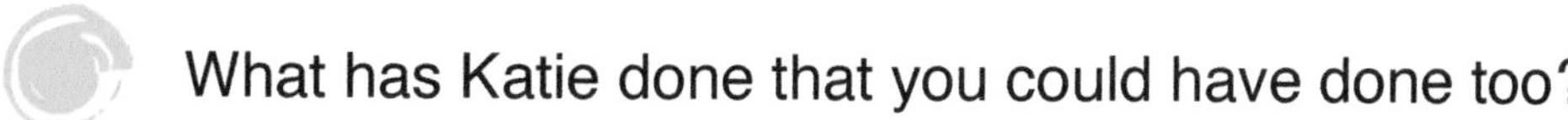

- How else would you improve Katie's answer?

You could use coloured highlighters to show the things that you like, the things that you don't like, and the things that you like but would change in some way.

I am bending down to tighten my camels' harness when the first gust of sand slap's my cheek. I look up, and suddenly the dunes are heaving like water. The camel lowers her head and walks on the sand whipping her legs, sometimes faster and sometimes more slowly. I feel proud of her, but also afraid. The dessert is on the move. Will I lose my way?

I can still see the sun through a gap in the clouds, but the gap is closing. The evening light is red. I think of my sisters back home. Sandstorms are dangerous. Will I see them again?

Already my nostrils are clogged with sand. I pull my scarf across my mouth and breathe deeply, but sand races round the sides and into my lungs. I cough painfully. My eyelids are screwed tight, but the rasping wind struggles to drag them open again.

I can hear nothing except the ripping of the strong wind, like a hundred-mile canvas being torn from end to end, although I should be terrified by now, the swaying tread of my camel, onward, onward, tells me that everything will be alright.

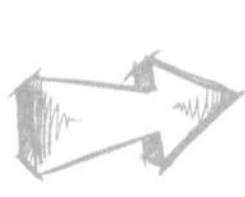

DON'T TURN THE PAGE UNTIL YOU'VE FINISHED HIGHLIGHTING AND TAKING NOTES!

Let's look at each paragraph separately.

I am bending down to tighten my camels' harness when the first gust of sand slap's my cheek. I look up, and suddenly the dunes are heaving like water. The camel lowers her head and walks on the sand whipping her legs, sometimes faster and sometimes more slowly. I feel proud of her, but also afraid. The dessert is on the move. Will I lose my way?

Katie gets straight into the action, which is usually a good choice, and there's a powerful sensory image – "**sand slaps my cheek**" – in the very first sentence.

There are some great verbs (words for actions), such as "**slaps**", "**heaving**" and "**whipping**".

These are good choices because they help the reader to imagine exactly what is going on.

Katie is already doing everything that the question asks for, including referring to the character's thoughts and emotions.

The first sentence contains two mistakes with apostrophes.
The harness *belongs to* ONE camel – this one! – so the apostrophe should come after "**camel**", giving us "**camel's**".

You would say "**camels'**" if several camels all had harnesses: "**the camels' harnesses**".

"**Slaps**", meanwhile, is a verb (an action), not a noun (a thing), and it doesn't possess anything. Therefore, it shouldn't have an apostrophe.

This camel is the protagonist's (main character's) only companion in this scene, and very important to him. This might be brought out better by giving her a name. This would also save you from having to repeat the word "**camel**" so often.

Katie's second sentence is short and direct, and almost excellent. However, the simile "**like water**" isn't as clear as it might be. Sometimes water "**heaves**", but more often it just sits there!

If you want to suggest that the sand dunes seem to surge and shift all around, it's no good if your reader sees "**like water**" and imagines a muddy puddle. "**Like a restless ocean**", for example, would create a much clearer and more dramatic image in the reader's mind.

A simile makes a description vivid by saying that one thing is similar to another, using "**like**" or "**as ... as**":

You snore like a walrus!

You snore as loudly as a walrus!

There will be opportunities to work closely with similes later in this course.

The next sentence needs a fair bit of re-jigging. Does the camel "**walk on the sand**", or does she "**walk on, the sand whipping her legs**"?

We need a comma to make clear that it's the second option.

You should practise reading your sentences out loud, listening to where you naturally pause.

Where you pause briefly, *like this*, it's likely that you need a comma.

Where there's a longer pause, you'll probably need another form of punctuation: perhaps a full stop, question mark, colon, dash or semicolon.

Try reading my previous paragraph ("**Where there's a longer ...**") out loud. Compare how long you pause for different kinds of punctuation mark.

Where do you breathe?

Choosing between punctuation marks can be tricky, but there will be help with this later in the course.

The verb "**walks**" is fine, but it isn't very interesting. Katie should consider whether another verb might be more powerful. In this case, the camel is pushing on through horrible conditions, and probably not enjoying the experience. "**Strides**" or "**trudges**" would convey its mood better.

Meanwhile, does "**sometimes faster and sometimes more slowly**" refer to the camel or the sand? If it's the sand, Katie could convey the same idea with the word "**surge**":

 "**the violently surging sand**".

Or, to avoid too many "**-ing**" words, "**whipping her legs in violent surges**".

If you can find a less wordy way to convey an idea, this will usually make your writing much more pleasant to read, as well as easier to understand.

Katie's last three sentences are simple but effective. However, watch out! "The dessert is on the move" seems to be referring to a wobbly jelly...

... when Katie meant to use the word "desert".

The missing comma in "**walks on the sand**" and the incorrect spelling of "**desert**" are both examples of how English mistakes can actually change the meaning of your writing. Spelling and grammar matter!

Here's the paragraph again, with all the corrections and improvements that I've suggested:

I am bending down to tighten Anya's harness when the first gust of sand slaps my cheek. I look up, and suddenly the dunes are heaving like a restless ocean. The camel lowers her head and strides on, the sand whipping her legs in violent surges. I feel proud of her, but also afraid. The desert is on the move. Will I lose my way?

Here's the next paragraph from Katie's work:

I can still see the sun through a gap in the clouds, but the gap is closing. The evening light is red. I think of my sisters back home. Sandstorms are dangerous. Will I see them again?

There are some **splendid** ideas here, but they could be expressed better.

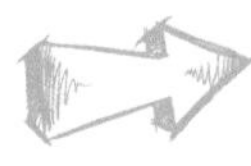

The first sentence contains a powerful image, but it's quite wordy and repeats "**gap**". "**Clouds are tightening around the sun**" would be much more direct, and would add to the emotion of the passage by subtly implying that the sun, like the protagonist, is feeling trapped.

"**Red**" in the second sentence could be a lot more specific, as well as more beautiful. What kind of red would the evening light be? The sandstorm would block out some of the light and probably tint it with orange. These two ideas could be conveyed by the phrase "**dull and rusty**".

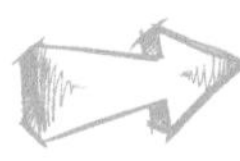

There's nothing wrong with simple, direct sentences such as "**I think of my sisters back home.**" Sometimes an idea is most powerful when it isn't cluttered up with descriptive words. On the other hand, "**sandstorms are dangerous**" is a very obvious statement. Either the reader has worked this out already, or they are beyond hope! Telling people things that they should already know is most likely to annoy them. This isn't a sentence for Katie to improve: it's a sentence to cross out.

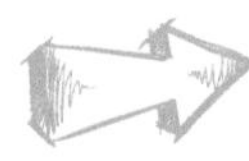

Lastly, "**Will I see them again?**" is fine in its own right, but feels repetitive because the first paragraph also ended with a question mark. This could be expressed as an indirect question: "**I wonder whether I will see them again**". It might even be joined to the previous sentence:

"... and wonder whether I will see them again."

Put these things together, and we have a much better paragraph:

Clouds are tightening around the sun. The evening light is dull and rusty. I think of my sisters back home and wonder whether I will see them again.

Good editing usually makes things shorter.

Already my nostrils are clogged with sand. I pull my scarf across my mouth and breathe deeply, but sand races round the sides and into my lungs. I cough painfully. My eyelids are screwed tight, but the rasping wind struggles to drag them open again.

This is a really good paragraph. It's full of images that show us how the narrator feels, mixed in with plenty of action: as he pulls the scarf over his mouth, as the sand "**races**" (great verb) past it, and as his eyelids fight with the wind.

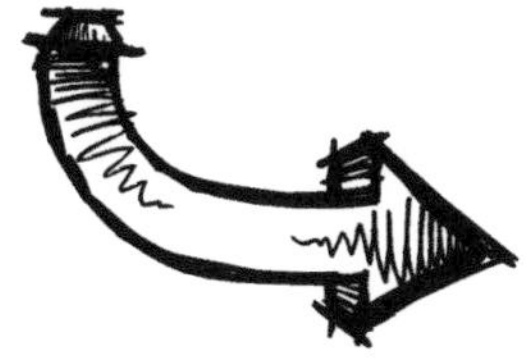

See how much can happen in a piece of writing, without there being a complex plot!

The only things that need correcting are a couple of repetitions: "**sand**" and the "**, but**" construction each appear twice.

Sometimes you will repeat yourself deliberately, for a good reason.

For example, repetition can emphasise the difference between two contrasting ideas:

"Once upon a time I was the richest man in Scotland. Once upon a time I was the most miserable man in the world."

However, if you repeat yourself by accident, this can be distracting for the reader. Their brain will search for a reason, without finding it. Avoid this by choosing an alternative word, or by restructuring a sentence.

The first "**sand**" isn't necessary, because the reader will know what is blocking the boy's nostrils. By removing this word, Katie can make space to add another sensory detail, for example by saying that his nose is "**sore**".

The first "**but**" could become "**and straight away**".

Already my nostrils are clogged and sore. I pull my scarf across my mouth and breathe deeply, and straight away sand races round the sides and into my lungs. I cough painfully. My eyelids are screwed tight, but the rasping wind struggles to drag them open again.

Now let's look at Katie's final paragraph:

I can hear nothing except the ripping of the strong wind, like a hundred-mile canvas being torn from end to end, although I should be terrified by now, the swaying tread of my camel, onward, onward, tells me that everything will be alright.

We don't need the adjective "**strong**," because it's obvious from "**ripping**".

Treat adjectives with respect! When they are carefully chosen, they can be an effective descriptive tool. Unnecessary adjectives, on the other hand, are distracting and make your writing clunky.

Compare these sentences:

The tired man heaved his heavy bag through the crumbling stone doorway.

The man heaved his bag through the crumbling doorway.

The first sentence might look fancy, but does it tell us much that we can't guess from the second one?

When in doubt, simplicity is usually your best bet.

The comma after "**end to end**" shows a mistake called comma-splicing. This is where you should use a full stop to separate two independent clauses, but put a comma instead.

In this case, the phrase "**although I should be terrified by now**" belongs with the camel's swaying: the storm ought to be very scary, but the camel calms the boy down. It isn't part of the discussion of the wind's noise. "**The wind is noisy, although I should be terrified by now**" would not make sense.

When one idea ends and another one begins, and when there is no connecting word such as "**and**", it is usually best to put a full stop.

When in doubt, bear in mind that short sentences can be easier to read than long ones.

Apart from these things, the paragraph is very effective. It adds to the emotional arc of the piece – the way that it follows the character's changing feelings – because the boy has become increasingly worried in the previous paragraphs, then calms down in this one.

The simile "**like a hundred-mile canvas**" creates an awesome impression of the wind's "**ripping**" sound, while "**onward, onward**" uses repetition to help us imagine the camel's loping steps and how the boy is willing it on.

I can hear nothing except the ripping of the wind, like a hundred-mile canvas being torn from end to end. Although I should be terrified by now, the swaying tread of my camel, onward, onward, tells me that everything will be alright.

KATIE'S IMPROVED ANSWER

It's time to put Katie's improved paragraphs together and see what a really good description might look like:

I am bending down to tighten Anya's harness when the first gust of sand slaps my cheek. I look up, and suddenly the dunes are heaving like a restless ocean. The camel lowers her head and strides on, the sand whipping her legs in violent surges. I feel proud of her, but also afraid. The desert is on the move. Will I lose my way?

Clouds are tightening around the sun. The evening light is dull and rusty. I think of my sisters back home and wonder whether I will see them again.

Already my nostrils are clogged and sore. I pull my scarf across my mouth and breathe deeply, and straight away sand races round the sides and into my lungs. I cough painfully. My eyelids are screwed tight, but the rasping wind struggles to drag them open again.

I can hear nothing except the ripping of the wind, like a hundred-mile canvas being torn from end to end. Although I should be terrified by now, the swaying tread of my camel, onward, onward, tells me that everything will be alright.

IMPROVING YOUR ANSWER

Now that you've seen how Katie's answer can be improved, let's consider how these lessons can be applied to your work.

- Which things in your answer do you want to leave as they are?
- Which things are mostly good, but need to be changed a bit?
- Which things should be crossed out?
- What could be added in to make it better?

If there isn't enough space to write notes in the margins of your first answer, you can use this space here:

Now it's time to write an improved version.

FOLLOW-UP EXERCISE 1

Here is a similar task to help you practise the things you've learnt in this pack.

THIS PHOTOGRAPH SHOWS ORCAS HUNTING SEA LIONS:

Imagine that you are one of the sea lions. Describe the situation and convey some of your thoughts and emotions, using the present tense. Your work should fit within the writing space provided.

FOLLOW-UP EXERCISE 2

THIS PHOTOGRAPH SHOWS A HOUSE AFTER THE FIRST SNOWFALL OF WINTER:

Imagine that you wake up inside this house and open the window. Describe what happens and what you see, conveying some of your thoughts and emotions. Use the present tense. Your work should fit within the writing space provided.

CREATING BEAUTIFUL WORD-IMAGES

This pack will show you how to create original, powerful descriptive images using the five senses.

THE FIVE SENSES

This pack will show you how to create original, powerful descriptive images using the five senses.

There are five principal senses:

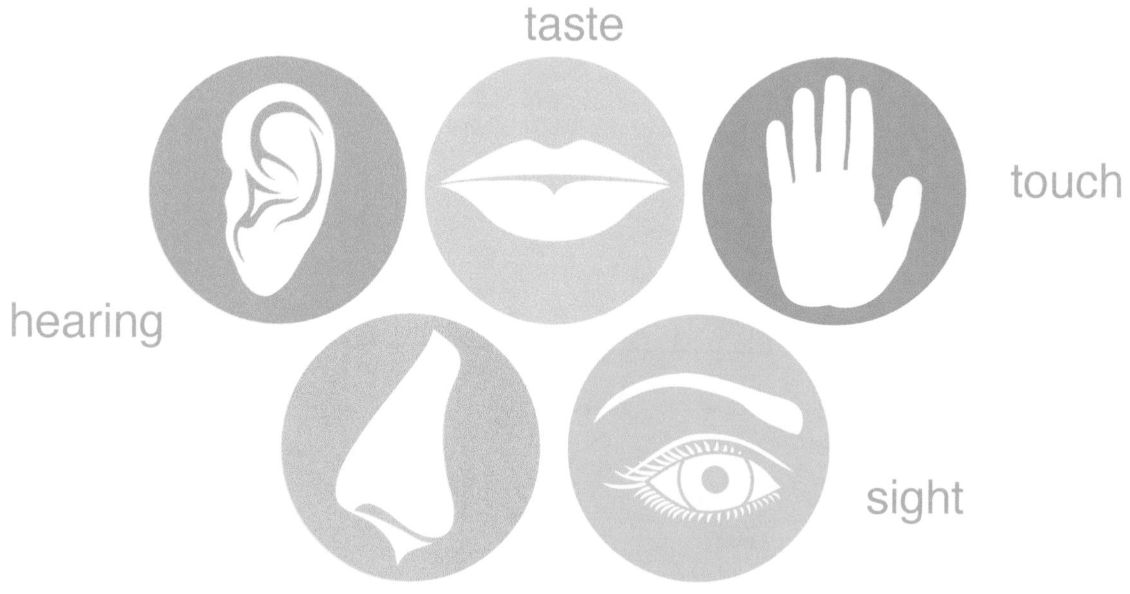

A scientist might point out that other senses deserve a mention, such as your sense of balance, and **proprioception**: the sense of space that enables you to put a biscuit in your mouth with your eyes closed. However, the common list of five gives us plenty to be getting on with.

HOW SENSORY IMAGERY MAKES A DIFFERENCE

Think about these two sentences:

Samuel enjoyed eating the biscuit, which reminded him of his childhood.

The biscuit snapped between Samuel's teeth and his mouth filled with the taste of cinnamon and cherry: the flavours of his childhood.

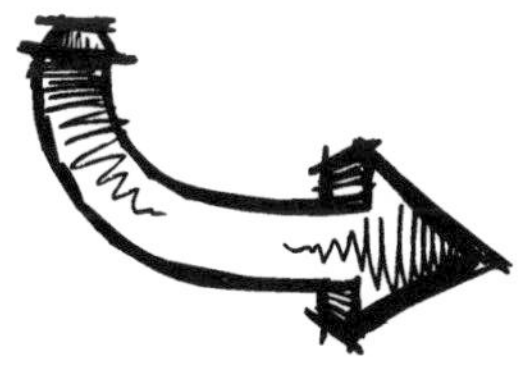

Both sentences convey the same core information: that Samuel ate a biscuit, which made him think of his youth.

However, while the first sentence presents these things as objective facts, the second sentence makes the experience subjective by binding it up with our own memories. It appeals to our senses, so that we remember our own experiences of cinnamon and cherry flavours and our awareness of how a biscuit snaps when we bite into it.

By the end of the sentence, which shows Samuel feeling nostalgic for the past, we are likely to enjoy a share of that nostalgia ourselves, mixing our own memories of childhood with Samuel's.

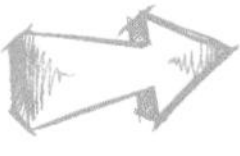

Writing like this transforms a character from a name on the page into a real person, who lives in the reader's imagination.

The same can be true for non-character descriptions – of places, for example:

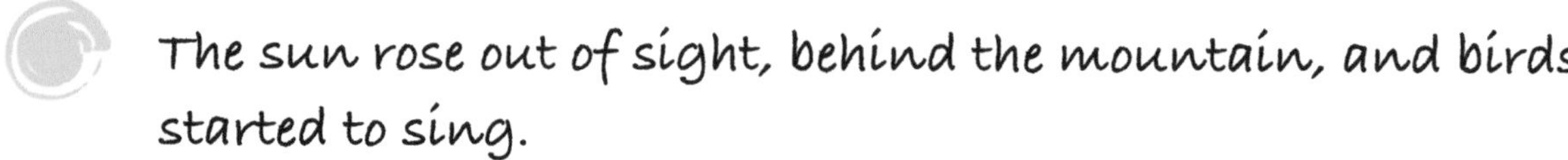

The sun rose out of sight, behind the mountain, and birds started to sing.

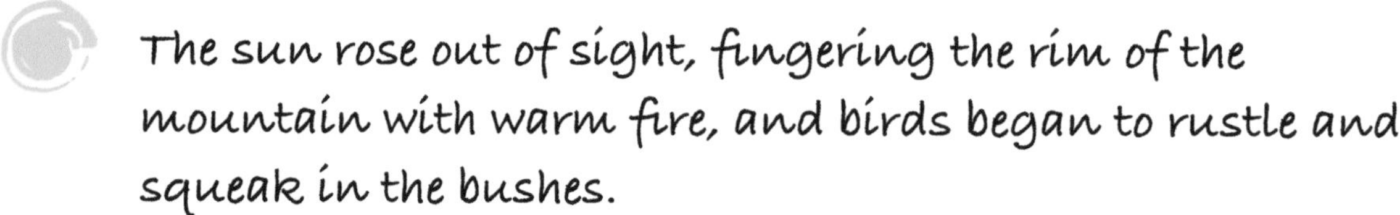

The sun rose out of sight, fingering the rim of the mountain with warm fire, and birds began to rustle and squeak in the bushes.

These are both good sentences: either might be at home in a finished piece of writing.

However, the second sentence is much more vivid.

“**Warm fire**” paints a very precise picture, with “**fingering**” suggesting that the light flickers into view here and there, as though a vast hand is groping its way up behind the hill.

This is an example of personification: a kind of metaphor that describes a thing as though it is alive.

"**Rustle and squeak**" is much more interesting than "**sing**": these are specific sounds for the reader to imagine. More importantly, they are not obvious choices. When a word or phrase is a little surprising, but precise and well-chosen, your attention is drawn to it and your imagination gets to work.

It's important not to overload a description with sensory images. Use them carefully, and the reader will imagine themselves in the scene or character. Add too much, and the annoying thought, *this writer is being clever*, will pull them straight back out again:

The biscuit snapped between Samuel's teeth and crumbled to warm, sweet mush, and his mouth filled with the taste of cinnamon and cherry while smells of baking wafted across from the oven: the rich flavours of his childhood.

This is likely to be too much!

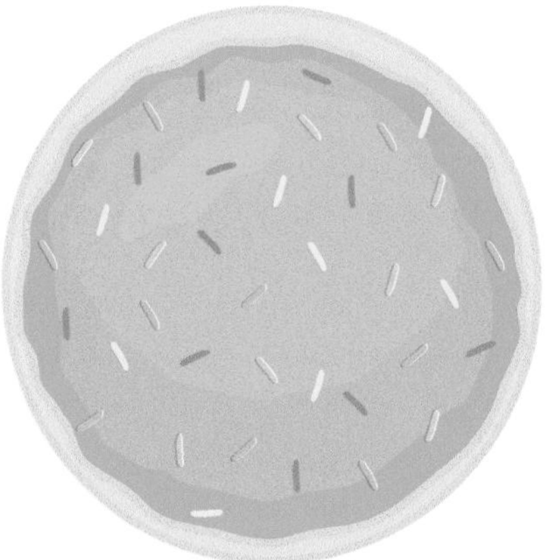

EXERCISE 1

Re-write the following sentences using sensory images. Try not to change the overall meaning and structure of the sentences too much.

Experiment with different senses: don't get too used to using sight and sound!

Afterwards, you'll have the chance to compare your ideas with mine.

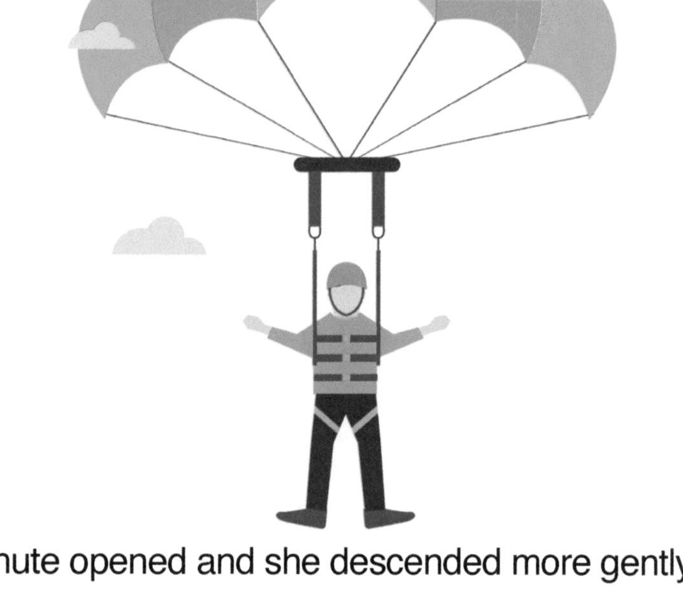

She fell quickly, until her parachute opened and she descended more gently.

....

....

....

As I was wading across the river, a fish leapt from the water nearby.

....

....

....

My brother is eating popcorn on the sofa while he plays a computer game.

....

....

....

Above my head, a squirrel jumped from one branch to another.

....

....

....

The ship slid down the ramp and into the water, where it floated for the first time.

....

....

....

As soon as the door opened, I could tell that my grandpa had been baking croissants.

....

....

....

EXERCISE 1: EXAMPLE ANSWERS

Here are some example sentences based on the prompts given above. Just because my responses are different from yours, this doesn't mean that they are better!

If these examples give you new ideas, you might like to have another go.

She fell quickly, until her parachute opened and she descended more gently.

The wind surged past her with tearing, painful force, until the world stopped moving with a bump and the gentle tug of her harness dangled her in space.

This focuses on physical feelings: in other words, the sense of touch. There are a number of words beginning with "**p**" and "**b**" consonants, also called plosives. For some readers, this repeated sound may help to create a sense of tumbling and bumpiness.

There are infinite possibilities. Here's an example using sight (visual) imagery:

The sky flashed all round in a kaleidoscope of grey and blue and of bright light, until her vision jolted and settled on the arc of the faraway horizon.

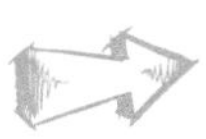

As I was wading across the river, a fish leapt from the water nearby.

My thoughts were far away, lulled by the sloshing of water in my trouser legs, when I was brought back to awareness by the swish and smack of a small, muscular body breaching the surface nearby.

Notice how this links sound imagery to the narrator's state of mind, by describing a hypnotic state brought on by the sounds of the river. It also uses sibilance: repeated "**s**" sounds, which are well suited to descriptions of water.

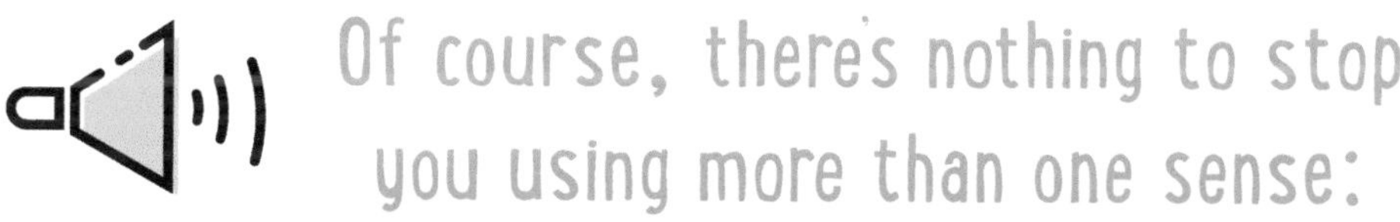

Of course, there's nothing to stop
you using more than one sense:

The cold misery of the water was already working its way up my thighs when I was stopped still by a somersaulting streak of airborne light.

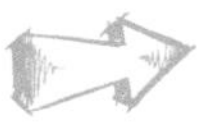

My brother is eating popcorn on the sofa while he plays a computer game.

The rustle of his hand rummaging in the carton is interspersed with the shriek and whizz of computer-generated missiles.

Sound is an obvious sense to focus on here, and these are quiet commonplace choices; but they are still effective.

Above my head, a squirrel jumped from one branch to another.

A fast-moving blur of grey draw my gaze up to the branches, where a squirrel compacted into a little round bundle as it landed, before scurrying away behind the trunk.

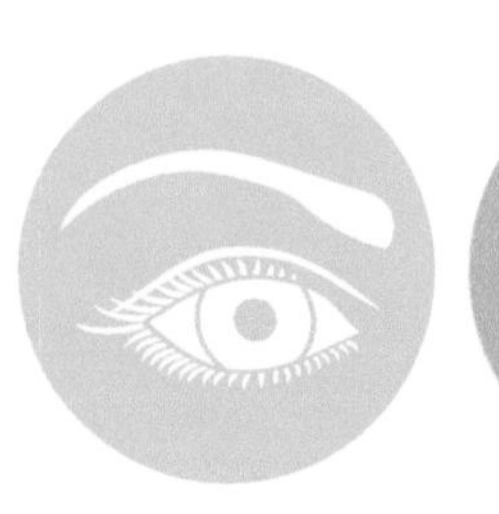

Sound would also be a powerful tool to describe this scene. You might choose to combine both senses in your sentence.

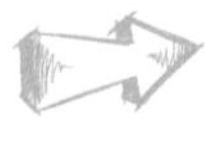

The ship slid down the ramp and into the water, where it floated for the first time.

The great hull eased down the ramp with a groan, and my mouth filled with the dry bitterness of concrete dust; then it hit the water with a great, booming "thwump".

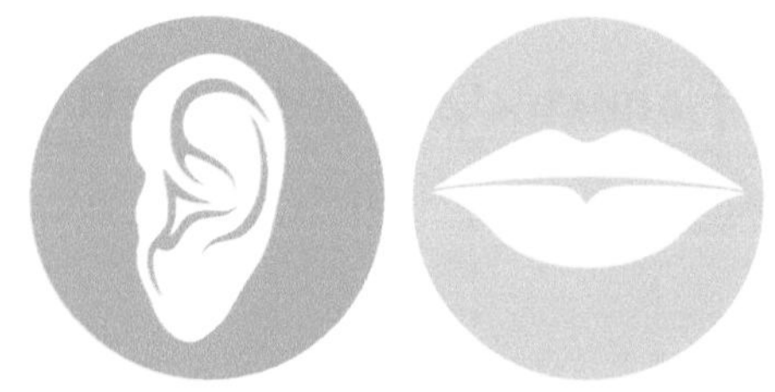

This example mixes sound and taste images to make the scene especially vivid.

Sometimes a made-up onomatopoeia (a word that sounds like the thing it describes) – such as "**thwump**" – can be effective. Make sure that your choice conveys the sound precisely, and be careful not to overuse this technique.

As soon as the door opened, I could tell that my grandpa had been baking croissants.

I drew back sharply from the doorway, the sweet, heavy pastry smoke already pawing at my cheeks.

The way in which you describe an event can change it significantly! In this version, it appears that the croissants have not so much been baked as incinerated.

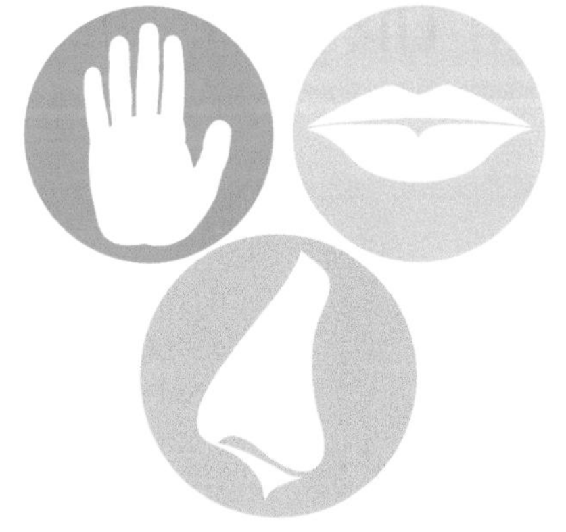

Notice how this focuses on touch imagery, but drops in a hint of taste/smell ("sweet"), to help the reader imagine a smell like burnt croissants –

rather than, say, a burnt loaf.

HOW TO BE ORIGINAL

The trouble with using the five senses is that it's difficult not to describe things in obvious ways that people have seen before. If you describe an engine "roaring", or a sunset "covering the fields in a rosy glow", it's more likely that your reader will think *Oh yeah, that again*, than that they will be inspired to imagine the scene as though they are there.

With a bit of work, you can come up with more creative descriptions – but this can be surprisingly difficult. If the engine isn't "**roaring**", perhaps it is "**purring**", "**spluttering**" or "**whirring**"...

but these are also very widely-used words to describe engine sounds.

Especially when you're describing a common experience, you'll often struggle to find simple and effective language that doesn't seem stale.

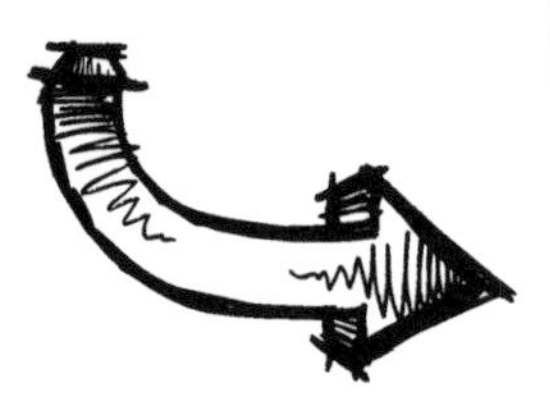

However, there is a simple technique for avoiding this problem.

Step 1: Imagine things in the simplest possible way.

The engine was making a loud noise.

Step 2: What would the most obvious sense(s) be?

Sound

Step 3: Ban this sense / these senses!

We can't use sound!

Step 4: Which senses are left?

Sight, touch, taste, smell

Step 5: Find a way to convey a similar idea without using the banned sense or senses.

Sight: The engine quivered, then started to shake wildly.

Smell/taste: The engine shot out foul-smelling fumes that rasped at the back of my throat.

Touch: As the engine came to life, the ground began to pulse beneath me.

These images are likely to leave a stronger – and much more memorable – impression in the reader's mind than a standard phrase such as "the engine roared to life".

As you can see from the example above, sometimes a different sense will also lead to a slightly different idea. Not all of the suggestions in step 5 clearly demonstrate "**a loud noise**", as described in step 1, although they all strongly imply it. **Your choices will depend on exactly what you want to communicate.**

The more commonplace a thing is, the more you should aim to use *less obvious senses* to describe it – and the more original and striking your descriptions are likely to be.

At the end of the day, if it's essential that the reader knows exactly what the engine sounds like, then of course you will need to use sound imagery!

The method I describe here should help when you want to be more original, but it shouldn't limit your freedom as a writer.

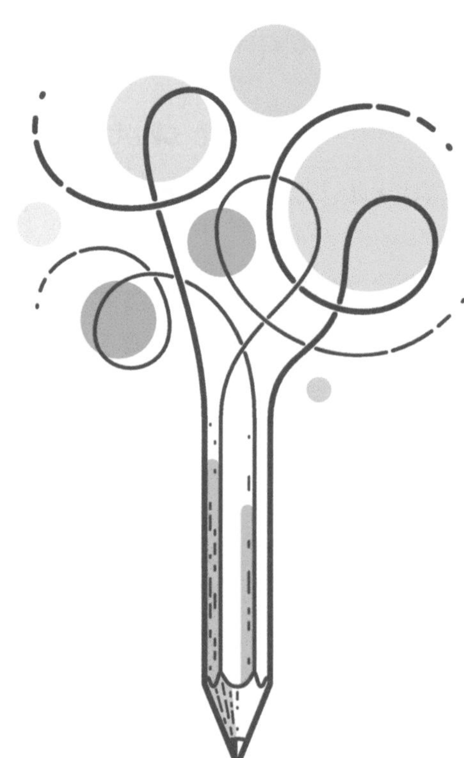

EXERCISE 2

The first step is to get used to identifying the most obvious sense(s), banning them, and working out which are left: steps 2 to 4.

My suggested answers follow the questions.

1. The cat was scratching the door.

Most obvious sense(s): ....

Remaining senses: ....

2. The cake was ready.

Most obvious sense(s): ....

Remaining senses: ....

3. The fighter jet flew over, just above the roof of my house.

Most obvious sense(s): ....

Remaining senses: ....

4. The painting shows a man herding cattle.

Most obvious sense(s): ....

Remaining senses: ....

5. The author is writing with an old pen.

Most obvious sense(s): ....

Remaining senses: ....

EXERCISE 2: EXAMPLE ANSWERS

This isn't a matter of right and wrong: you may disagree!

1 The cat was scratching the door.

Most obvious sense(s): *sight, sound*

Remaining senses: *touch, taste, smell*

2 The cake was ready.

Most obvious sense(s): *smell, taste*

Remaining senses: *sight, sound, touch*

3 The fighter jet flew over, just above the roof of my house.

Most obvious sense(s): *sight, sound*

Remaining senses: *touch, taste, smell*

4 The painting shows a man herding cattle.

Most obvious sense(s): *sight*

Remaining senses: *touch, sound, smell, taste*

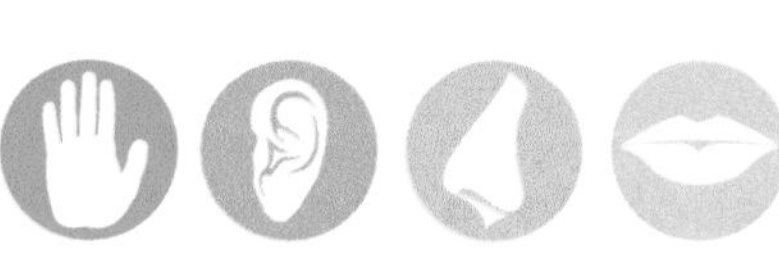

5 The author is writing with an old pen.

Most obvious sense(s): *sight*

Remaining senses: *sound, taste, touch, smell*

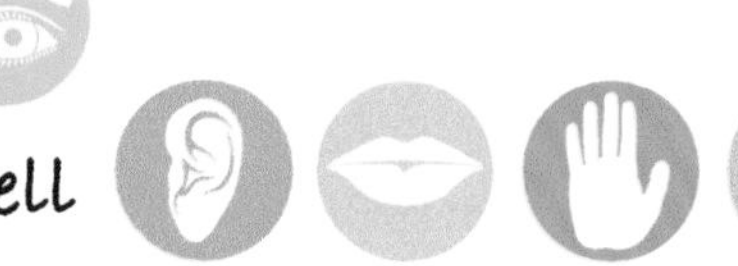

EXERCISE 3

Now it's time to practise step 5, using the same examples.

In each case, you'll have the opportunity to write a description using an obvious sense, then with one of the remaining, less obvious senses.

Once again, there's space for your answers, after which I offer my own suggestions.

1 The cat was scratching the door.

Using an obvious sense: ....

....

....

Using a less obvious sense: ....

....

....

2 The cake was ready.

Using an obvious sense: ....

....

....

Using a less obvious sense: ....

....

....

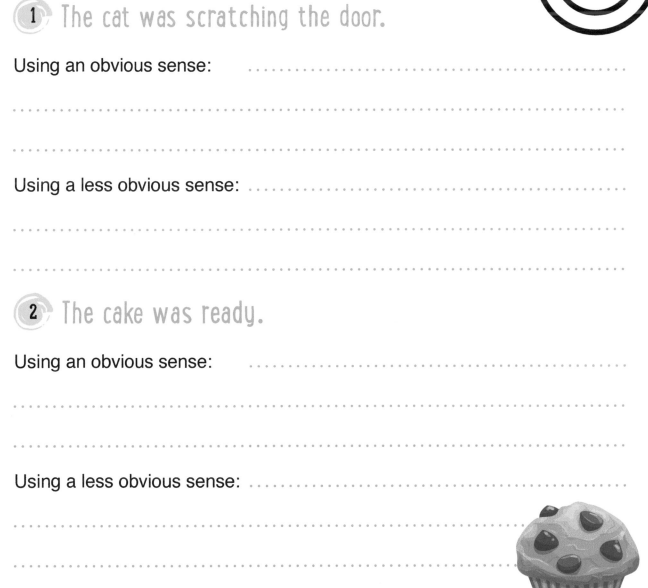

3 The fighter jet flew over, just above the roof of my house.

Using an obvious sense: ....

....

....

Using a less obvious sense: ....

....

....

4 The painting shows a man herding cattle.

Using an obvious sense: ....

....

....

Using a less obvious sense: ....

....

....

5 The author is writing with an old pen.

Using an obvious sense: ....

....

....

Using a less obvious sense: ....

....

....

EXERCISE 3: EXAMPLE ANSWERS

As always, remember that these are not 'the answers', and that your ideas might well be better.

1 The cat was scratching the door.

Using an obvious sense: With each downward tug of its claws, the cat sends a shiver of bright paint dust onto the floor.

Using a less obvious sense: I put my palm against the door and smiled as I felt the regular shudders that passed from tiny paws, through the woodwork and up the bones of my arm.

2 The cake was ready.

Using an obvious sense: I hovered above the cake, sucking in warm smells of cinnamon and sweetness.

Using a less obvious sense: As my knife passed through the cake, the two halves peeled apart and flopped onto the dish with a contented, bouncy slap.

3 The fighter jet flew over, just above the roof of my house.

Using an obvious sense: It passed overhead with only a dull rumble, but then the sound rushed over me like the roaring of a waterfall.

Using a less obvious sense: At first it was just a light tremble in my shoulder blades, but within seconds this had grown to a frantic shaking; then the force of rushing air pushed me backwards.

4 The painting shows a man herding cattle.

Using an obvious sense: The gallery's lighting caught the brush strokes on the animals' flanks and the man's stick, giving him the appearance of a conjurer, his wand drawing magic fire from their hides.

Using a less obvious sense: As I stare at the picture, my mind conjures humid smells of sweat and dung.

5 The author is writing with an old pen.

Using an obvious sense: Her hand moves across the page in a staccato motion, as the nib sticks and then gives way to pressure.

Using a less obvious sense: Harsh scratching is interspersed with squeaks, and with occasional quiet intervals when the ink flows as it should.

EXERCISE 4

It's unlikely that you're following this course in order to write single sentences.

In this exercise, you'll be given two scenarios to describe in short paragraphs, using as much sensory imagery as possible – even if the result may seem a little overcooked!

You don't need to use less obvious senses on every occasion, but this is a good chance to experiment with them and see how they can make your writing better.

You can write in the present or past tense, as you prefer.

A lorry drives through a puddle and splashes you with water.

....

....

....

....

....

....

....

....

....

A deer moves through a forest.

EXERCISE 4: EXAMPLE ANSWERS

See how my choices compare with yours.

A lorry drives through a puddle and splashes you with water.

A truck careered round the corner, its engine groaning. I leapt back and my heel jarred painfully against a raised cobblestone, almost toppling me into the gutter. As I regained my balance, the nearest tyre swept up a wide fan of puddle water and flung it against my face, so hard that my cheeks stung. The lorry swooshed away, leaving me bent over on the pavement, coughing out the taste of oily water and exhaust.

This description focuses on sound, touch and taste. It's possible to create a remarkably strong visual picture without making any special effort to describe what things look like.

 A deer moves through a forest.

Something shifts between the trees: a flickering outline, shadow in shadow, silent as a spirit. Then, with a hiss of shuffling leaves, the silhouette clarifies itself and steps into the glade, moonlight flickering in its antlers. Its head turns to left and right, slowly, its soft muzzle snuffling the dusty smells of a summer evening. Then, with a patter of hooves on hollow ground, it is gone, and nothing moves except the sighing breeze.

This focuses on sight, sound and smell, but there is also touch: directly, in the reference to the deer's "**soft muzzle**", and implicitly when its hooves touch the "**hollow ground**".

There's a lot of alliteration with "**s**" and "**h**" sounds, helping to create a whispering, dreamlike atmosphere.

Both these example answers have the same basic narrative: a lorry or a deer arrives, does something, then departs. However, they use this structure to achieve very different things.

FOLLOW-UP EXERCISE 1

These optional follow-up tasks offer further practice.

Here are some scenarios to describe in single sentences:

1. An astronaut drinks coffee.

2. A hawk grabs a small bird in flight.

3. An old person is asleep.

4 A child skims a stone across a lake.

....

....

....

5 You place the last piece in a jigsaw.

....

....

....

FOLLOW-UP EXERCISE 2

Here are some scenarios to describe in short paragraphs:

1. A building is on fire.

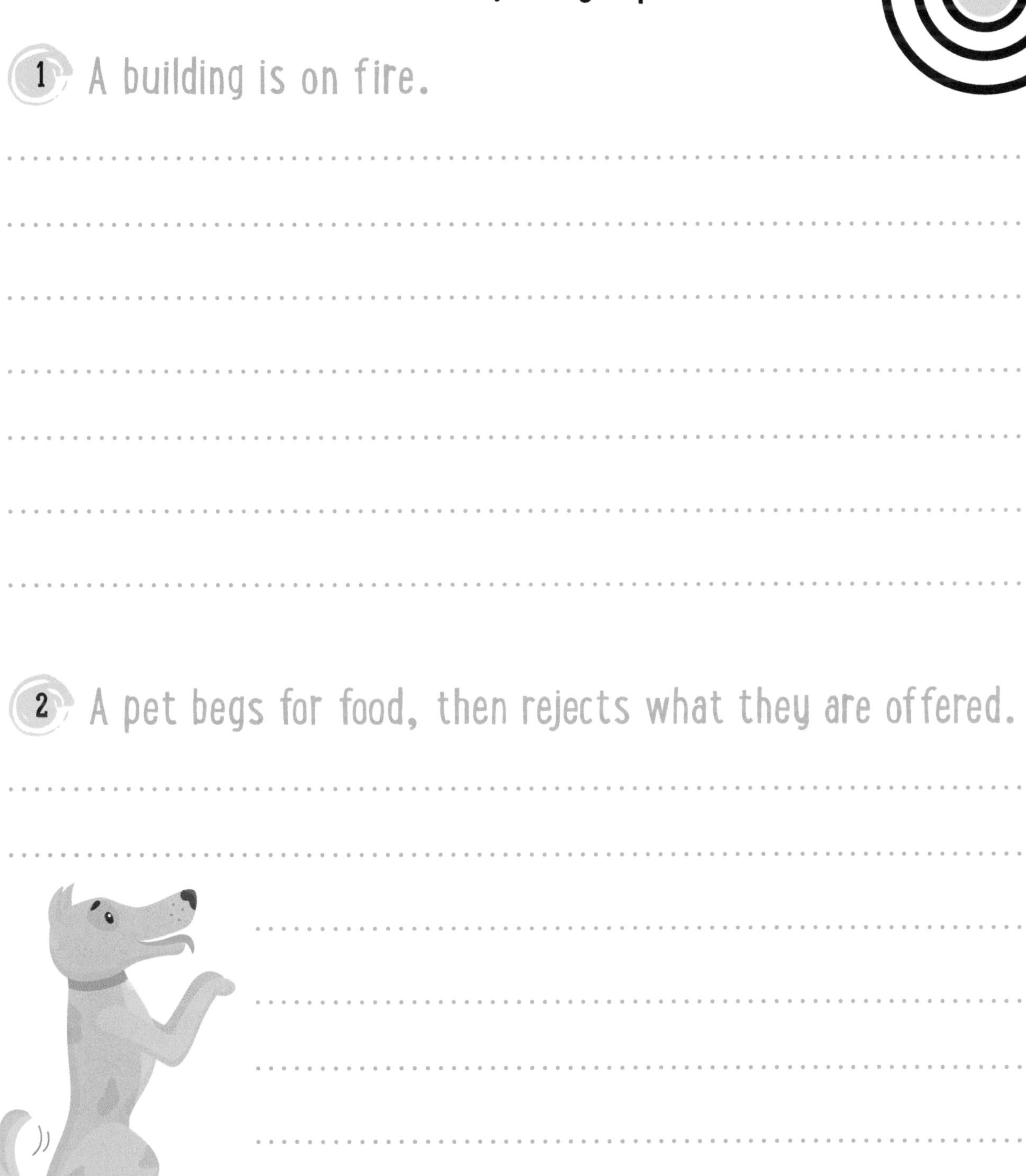

2. A pet begs for food, then rejects what they are offered.

blank page

WRITING A SHORT STORY

This pack will show you how to build an effective short story around a single character and a simple plot.

ON THE MOUNTAIN

This pack will show you how to build an effective short story around a single character and a simple plot.

Pack 2 will have given you some ideas for writing effective descriptions, while Pack 1 will have got you thinking about characterisation and scene-setting.

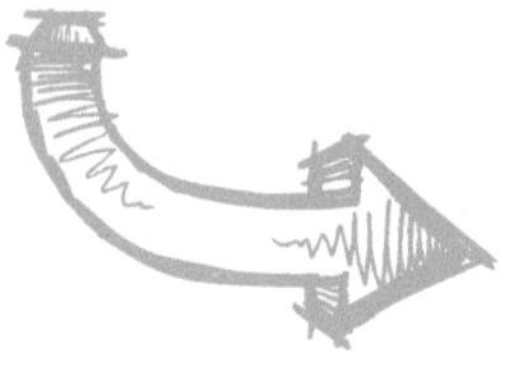

By now, you're probably keen to start putting these ideas together into a story.

This pack will give you the chance to have a go:

 writing at greater length

 and with a simple plot.

You'll be describing a situation quite similar to the scenario in Pack 1: a person who is alone in a wild and dangerous place. **This will give you the opportunity to adapt and improve some of the ideas you developed in that piece of writing.**

IT IS EVENING. YOU HAVE LOST YOUR WAY IN THE MOUNTAINS AND ARE BECOMING DESPERATE. YOU FEEL LONELY AND TIRED, AND ARE AFRAID OF PASSING A NIGHT IN THE WIND AND THE COLD. THEN YOU COME ACROSS THIS EMPTY HUT:

Write a short story based on this picture, in which you describe the experience of being alone in the mountains and of finding shelter. The story should end when you go to sleep.

You must write in the past tense and in the first person: for example, "**I was ...**".

Write between one and two pages.

PLANNING YOUR STORY

Perhaps the most important rule for planning a short story is to keep it as simple as possible.

It's very easy to include too much plot, even in a simple task like this, so that you end up saying "**this happened**, **then this**, **then this**, **then this**," and so on, leaving you little room for the character-building and description that can make your writing powerful.

I suggest that you ask yourself the following questions. There are many other things that you could consider, but these will offer you a strong framework.

I've given my own answers, after which there's space to write your own. **Try to make yours different from mine!**

You wouldn't have time to plan in such detail in a writing exam, for example, but it's very useful to do so when you can.

1 Who is the protagonist (main character)?

To write about a character effectively, you need to have a clear idea of who they are. Their behaviour, and therefore the plot and mood of your story, will be driven by this. You shouldn't include lots of back-story (personal history) in your writing, but feel free to think about it here.

How did they arrive in your story? What has happened, and how does it relate to their personality? Which of their character traits and interests/skills are likely to be relevant?

My ideas:

Maria is a teenage girl whose family lives in a nearby valley. She often walks alone in the mountains, but this time she left home in a hurry after an argument, without packing a map, food or proper clothing, and without her phone. After a while she lost her way, but she did not want to turn back. She is a stubborn person and always finds it difficult to admit that she might be wrong. She does not like to change her decisions. She knows a lot about mountain animals and plants.

Your ideas:

If you like to draw, you might find it useful to sketch your protagonist.

2 Where and when does the story begin?

Remember that your ideas have to match the requirements of the question – for example, **that it is evening**.

My ideas:

The story has a modern-day setting. It is spring time, and still cold in the high mountains. The narrative starts with Maria, very tired, dragging herself up a steep slope, with the mountaintops seeming to be near, though actually they are still far away. The sun is already out of sight behind the hills.

Your ideas:

3 What is the dramatic/emotional climax?

A story of this length should usually focus on one main event. This gives a three-part structure:

- Building up to the event
- The event itself
- The aftermath of the event

Where there is a single main character, you are likely to be particularly interested in exploring how their personality shapes and is shaped by the main event.

My ideas:

The main event is when Maria finds the hut, just as it is becoming dark, and looks for a way in.

Your ideas:

....

....

....

....

4 What is the mood, and does it change?

Your ideas about the atmosphere of the story may well change as you write it. However, it's helpful to have an idea before you start.

My ideas:

The mood is calm initially, with Maria feeling uneasy and alone rather than afraid, her bleak mood matching the landscape. There's a period of frantic hope as she finds the hut and hopes that she can get in; then calm returns, but with mixed feelings of comfort and cold, as well as guilt.

Your ideas:

Will there be any other characters – and if so, any dialogue?

You always need to consider this – even if, as in this case, the answer is likely to be "**no**"!

Although the hut is "**empty**" (see the instructions above), it is possible that somebody finds your character there; or that they pass another walker in the early evening. **Be careful, though**: introducing extra characters unnecessarily often leads a story off course, pulling focus from the things that matter.

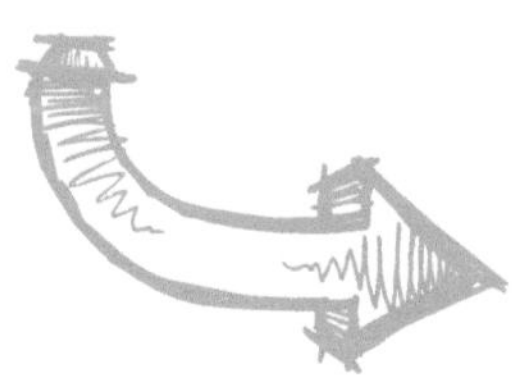

Bear in mind that too much dialogue can easily turn a story into a play script. All things are possible for a good writer, but it can be difficult to maintain a reader's interest when all your characters do is talk to each other.

My ideas:

No other characters.

Your ideas:

QUICK PLANNING (OPTIONAL)

**If I had to plan quickly
- for example, in a writing exam -
I would go through the thought process above,
but quite rapidly, and only writing quick notes.
I would rely on my memory to hold on to many
of the details.**

My quick plan might look something like this:

I am Maria. Left home after argument, no phone etc. Now lost, feel uneasy. Getting dark.

See hut. Rush to reach it as gets dark. Hopeful, then scared it will be locked. Find way in, relieved.

Comfort/cold, guilt/gratitude as go to sleep.

You might like to have a go at writing your own quick plan in the following space:

....

....

....

....

....

....

....

YOUR STORY (FIRST VERSION)

Now it's time to have a go. You'll have another opportunity later in this pack.

Try not to use more than the writing space provided.

MY STORY

Here is my attempt at a story. Think about how it compares to yours. *Why have I made the choices that I have? Could I have made better ones?*

After you've read the story, I'll explain what I've done, section by section.

The root, which had looked so secure, came away with my weight and I staggered back and fell to my knees, still clutching it with both hands. Pebbles fled down the slope, bouncing from rock to rock with little snapping sounds. I tried to take stock of the near-vertical scree above me. Fifty metres more? Two hundred? Two peaks poked out above the lip, and beyond them was the darkening, indigo sky.

I eased myself to my feet and checked my watch. Eight o'clock. Behind me, the shadows of the valley would be glistening with pinpricks of light from cosy sitting rooms. I did not look back.

Where the scree ended, the spindly goat track started again. I shuffled up the slope on heavy legs that seemed more interested in dragging me backwards. I was staring at the ground in front of me, my breath heaving with each step. I could hear the "cronk, cronk" call of a raven overhead, but I didn't look up. My only interest was in putting the valley behind me, one step at a time. I hardly knew where I was going any more, and nor did I care.

I lost my footing again, tipped sideways and rolled forwards. Forwards?

Something cold was scraping my face and I could smell damp turf. The ground beneath my body was spongy, moulding itself to the pressure of my chest.

I lifted myself onto my knees, brushing wafers of iced snow from my cheeks and forehead. A wide expanse of meadow opened in front of me, interspersed with rounded domes of rock like the backs of drifting sea monsters. Beyond it, far away now, reared the two peaks, white and grey and forbidding. A light wind gusted across the plateau, and suddenly I felt the cold. Hugging myself where the straps of my rucksack should have been, I remembered that I had not brought it, and for the first time I felt scared, vulnerable and stupid.

Then I saw the hut, some five hundred metres away, its outline barely visible in the settling darkness.

I flung myself against the building's wall, furious with hope, scrabbling for an opening. I knew that I was shivering, but by now I was too desperate and excited to feel cold. From a distance the hut had seemed insubstantial. Now I found that it was all packed stone and tightly interlocking planks.

Before long, my hand had found the door. I rattled the latch madly, up and down, tugging and pushing. I launched my shoulder against the planks in final desperation, then sunk to my haunches, bruised, aching and ready to cry.

The breeze picked up, and as it did I heard a squeal and a dead slap somewhere above me. Jerking my head round, I could just make out the swaying silhouette of an open window shutter. All I can remember is a feeling of dread: dread of metal bars or another, locked shutter behind it.

And then my belly was on the ledge, my arms straining to hold my weight; and then my head was tipping into darkness, and in a flail of limbs I found myself sprawling deliciously in thick, warming straw.

It can't have been more than a few seconds before I was asleep.

YOUR THOUGHTS

- Now that you've written your own story and read my example, what are your thoughts?
- What ideas would you like to steal from this to improve your work?
- What would you change in my story, to make it better?

Here's some space for you to note down ideas, before we go on to look at the example story section by section:

MY STORY: SECTION BY SECTION

The root, which had looked so secure, came away with my weight and I staggered back and fell to my knees, still clutching it with both hands. Pebbles fled down the slope, bouncing from rock to rock with little snapping sounds. I tried to take stock of the near-vertical scree above me. Fifty metres more? Two hundred? Two peaks poked out above the lip, and beyond them was the darkening, indigo sky.

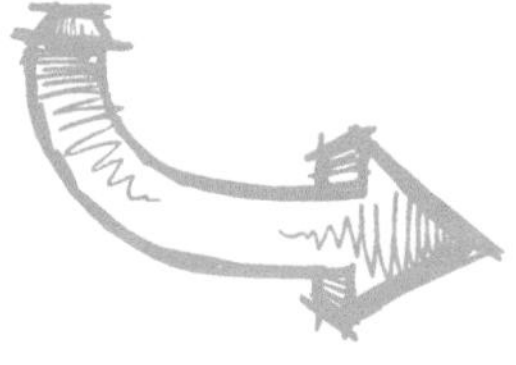

I start in the middle of events, without an introduction. Anything that the reader needs to know about the character can be explained – or even better, suggested – when it's necessary.

The first sentence sets up various important ideas. The protagonist feels confident in her ability, judging which holds are trustworthy by sight alone; but this confidence seems to be misplaced. The fact that she is still holding the broken root after her fall adds to the impression of confidence, because she must have gripped it very securely. The way that she staggers and falls, on the other hand, hints at her tiredness.

The pebbles are personified (made to seem alive) with the verb "**fled**", while the "**little snapping sounds**" are almost jolly. The mountain is made to seem full of life, as though it has a will of its own.

The rest of the paragraph builds an impression of Maria's uncertainty and of her vulnerability, as evening approaches in a landscape that dwarfs her.

You will have noticed that the story misses out much of my plan. All the information about why Maria is here has been left out. Even her name and sex aren't mentioned.

This doesn't matter. The plan means that I know what is going on and why, and ensures that the story will fit together coherently. I can drop hints about the past when these will help the reader relate to the character's emotions. Look at how I do this in the next paragraph:

I eased myself to my feet and checked my watch. Eight o'clock. Behind me, the shadows of the valley would be glistening with pinpricks of light from cosy sitting rooms. I did not look back.

The reader can draw their own conclusions about why Maria does not want to think about the "**cosy sitting rooms**" far below her. The simple sentence "**I did not look back**" carries more emotion than I would have achieved by explaining exactly what happened to her earlier on.

When you're deciding whether to include a piece of information, ask yourself two questions:

Without it, will the reader be confused?

If the answer to this is yes, you should include the information.

Will the emotional power of the story be increased or decreased if I include it?

Bear in mind that the more a reader has to use their imagination, the stronger the emotions that they are likely to feel. Your job is to help them imagine things in a certain way; not to do all the work for them.

Where the scree ended, the spindly goat track started again. I shuffled up the slope on heavy legs that seemed more interested in dragging me backwards. I was staring at the ground in front of me, my breath heaving with each step. I could hear the "cronk, cronk" call of a raven overhead, but I didn't look up. My only interest was in putting the valley behind me, one step at a time. I hardly knew where I was going any more, and nor did I care.

I lost my footing again, tipped sideways and rolled forwards. Forwards?

Something cold was scraping my face and I could smell damp turf. The ground beneath my body was spongy, moulding itself to the pressure of my chest.

This section is very descriptive and uses a range of senses: hearing, touch and sight.

Verbs such as shuffled, dragging and heaving give a strong sense of how Maria feels.

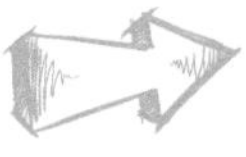

You may have noticed, however, that it uses few adjectives: in the first paragraph of the section, only spindly and heavy. It's a common mistake to think that descriptive writing involves putting an adjective in front of every noun!

The sentences are short and simple, reflecting the fact that the character's experience is also simple. She is focused on just one thing: a desperate desire to move forwards.

When you write in the first person, using "**I**", remember that your reader should only know what the narrator (the "**I**" voice) knows.

If you want to get around this and tell the reader something that the character doesn't know, you will need to be clever.

Sentences beginning:

 "I now know that …" or

 "What I didn't know at the time was that …", for example, can allow you to add **important extra information** when it is essential.

I lifted myself onto my knees, brushing wafers of iced snow from my cheeks and forehead. A wide expanse of meadow opened in front of me, interspersed with rounded domes of rock like the backs of drifting sea monsters. Beyond it, far away now, reared the two peaks, white and grey and forbidding. A light wind gusted across the plateau, and suddenly I felt the cold. Hugging myself where the straps of my rucksack should have been, I remembered that I had not brought it, and for the first time I felt scared, vulnerable and stupid.

Then I saw the hut, some five hundred metres away, its outline barely visible in the settling darkness.

When you're describing an experience that may not be familiar to your reader, it's helpful to use language that anybody can relate to easily. "**Wafers**" uses a single, easily understood word to show the crisp thinness of the pieces of snow stuck to Maria's face.

On the other hand, the unusual simile "**like the backs of drifting sea monsters**" helps to convey the spooky unreality of the scene. Because different people will have different mental images to match the term "**sea monster**", this simile will create a different picture in different people's minds; at the same time, "**rounded domes**" provides a bit of detail to keep people on the right track.

The right mix of descriptive words can be powerful. "**A light wind gusted**" combines two slightly contradictory ideas to convey a precise impression of how the wind is moving: it isn't strong, but it comes and goes in surges. The verb "**gusted**" suggests reserves of power, implying that there might be worse to come.

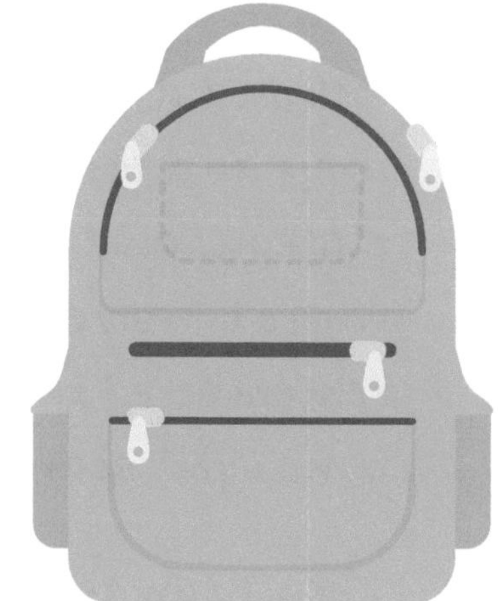

The section about the rucksack introduces a little more back-story at the point where it matters most. The reader learns that for some reason Maria left home unprepared, and this means that when she sees the hut, we share her realisation that unless she can get inside it, she will be exposed and without protection from the freezing night.

When Maria sees the hut, this is described very simply. This matches the way that strong emotions sometimes don't come at the moment of discovering an important thing: they come slightly afterwards. The reader sees what Maria sees, and has time to reach their own conclusions about it. **The sentence is given its own paragraph, and this is enough to demonstrate its importance.**

This is the section that most directly relates to the photograph at the top. As I wrote this story, I imagined Maria falling onto the plateau somewhere to the left of the hut, outside the image's border. Her home is down in the valley, between here and the range of peaks at the top of the photo. The two peaks that I describe are behind the photographer's position: perhaps behind their right shoulder. I took a few details – the grass and the thin patches of snow, and the compact little hut – and made them part of the story.

I flung myself against the building's wall, furious with hope, scrabbling for an opening. I knew that I was shivering, but by now I was too desperate and excited to feel cold. From a distance the hut had seemed insubstantial. Now I found that it was all packed stone and tightly interlocking planks.

Before long, my hand had found the door. I rattled the latch madly, up and down, tugging and pushing. I launched my shoulder against the planks in final desperation, then sunk to my haunches, bruised, aching and ready to cry.

The breeze picked up, and as it did I heard a squeal and a dead slap somewhere above me. Jerking my head round, I could just make out the swaying silhouette of an open window shutter. All I can remember is a feeling of dread: dread of metal bars or another, locked shutter behind it.

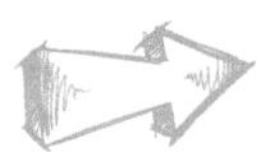

Between the end of the previous paragraph, "**its outline barely visible in the settling darkness**", and the beginning of this section, there is an obvious leap in time: Maria must already have covered the "**five hundred metres**" to the hut.

If part of your plot isn't important – just filler between things that matter – you should skip past it. To make this work, you need to do two things:

Start a new paragraph.

Make it immediately clear that this leap in time has happened. In this case, "**against the building's wall**" shows straight away that the narrative has skipped Maria's journey to the hut.

This section shows very strong emotions. Notice that they change: desperate hope, followed by desperate fear, then despair, then surprise and a glimmer of hope again; and then pessimism ("**dread**").

Writers sometimes look for multiple ways to show a single emotion. In this case, the whole section could have focused on fear, or hope, described in several ways. However, this is often boring, even annoying, to read. Instead, think about how your feelings might **change** in a stressful situation, and encourage the reader's mood to follow the same trajectory.

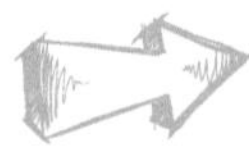

The last paragraph in this section uses a lot of words beginning with "**s**" – sibilant sounds – to create a sound world dominated by the wind and its ability to move things.

And then my belly was on the ledge, my arms straining to hold my weight; and then my head was tipping into darkness, and in a flail of limbs I found myself sprawling deliciously in thick, warming straw.

It can't have been more than a few seconds before I was asleep.

Repeated use of "**and**", especially to start sentences, can be lazy style. Here the word is used to show how things happen in quick succession, faster than the protagonist hopes or expects.

Again, emotions are shown changing rapidly, moving through desperate "**straining**" effort, helplessness (and probably fear) shown by "**tipping**" and "**flail**", then relief, comfort and relaxation.

You may have noticed that although my planning ideas mention a feeling of guilt at the end, I've left that out here so as not to over-complicate things.

Instead, the last paragraph is simple, to match the simplicity of dropping into happy sleep without effort.

ANOTHER EXAMPLE STORY ... WITH PROBLEMS!

It's easy to go off-track when writing a story like this. I've written a second example, to give you an idea of how this can happen.

This version uses the same character and situation as the example above. As you read it, try to work out where the problems are.

When you've read it, you'll have the opportunity to compare your criticisms with mine.

A grey, stony slope reached far above me into the cold, unwelcoming sky. An annoyingly cheerful bird sang nearby, but I ignored it. Out of sight, a couple of hundred metres to my left, a family of badgers were silently exploring the bouncy, needle-strewn ground outside their set.

I sighed, thinking back to the morning. For weeks, I had wanted to cut my hair short and get rid of the annoying, swishy, waist-long mane that took twenty minutes to dry and brush every day and made me feel like a little child. "But it's your crowning glory!" my mother had screamed, clutching her chest, the first time that I declared my intention to cut it. "You'll never manage to grow it back."

Dad, who usually stays out of things and lets Mum and me fight, had weighed in on her side. "You'll only regret it", he said, keeping his eyes fixed on the newspaper spread out in front of him.

This morning, after weeks of stewing over the unfairness of it all, I'd borrowed some old sheep shears from behind the boot room door, made a rough ponytail, and cut the whole lot off in one crunchy, satisfying snip.

Then the shouting had started. It hadn't seemed worth staying to fight. I'd been so angry that I hadn't packed anything – not my phone, not a coat, not any lunch; and certainly not anything as sensible as a map. All I carried with me was a burning sense that, in some way I hadn't clearly worked out for myself yet, I would make them regret it.

As I disappeared into the trees, my mother and father had looked at each other. "She'll be back for dinner," said Dad, without concern. "She just needs to blow off steam." Then he went back to his armchair.

Now I staggered up the slope as darkness began to fall, half my brain replaying the morning's events, half struggling to drive me forwards up the loose, dry surface despite the cold, the hunger and the thirst. It was so hard. I could imagine the little lights flickering on in cosy sitting rooms far below me, but I did not look back.

I lost my footing again, tipped sideways and rolled forwards. Something cold was scraping my face and I could smell damp, sweet turf. The ground beneath my body was spongy, moulding itself to the pressure of my tired chest.

I lifted myself onto my knees, brushing snow from my cheeks and forehead. A wide expanse of meadow opened in front of me. Beyond it, far away now, reared the two peaks, white and grey and forbidding. Hugging myself where the straps of my rucksack should have been, I remembered that I had not brought it, and now I felt scared, vulnerable and – for the first time – stupid.

Then I saw the hut, its outline barely visible in the settling darkness. I tried to run towards it, but my legs were so tired that I kept falling.

At last I flung myself against the building's wall. I searched all over, but couldn't find an entrance.

Then I heard an open shutter squeaking above me. I launched myself through the gap, and fell into thick, warming straw. It can't have been more than a few seconds before I was asleep.

YOUR THOUGHTS

- In your opinion, what are the weaknesses of this alternative story?
- Did you do similar things in your story, and if not, how did you avoid them?
- Does this version have any advantages over my other one?

Here's some space for jotting down your thoughts, before you read mine:

MY THOUGHTS

In my opinion, these are the main problems with this second story:

Key events aren't emotionally meaningful.

If the reader is going to share Maria's relief when she finds shelter, they have to care about her situation when she's in trouble; then they need enough information to help them relate to her feelings when she makes it to safety.

In this story, some time is given to setting up the situation on the mountain, but the flash-back to home pulls focus away from this. The crucial section where she finds the hut is dealt with very quickly: the reader barely has time to worry about whether she will find a way in, before she manages it. There's very little tension or emotional intensity in the narrative.

There's too much background information.

This story wants to be two stories. It tries to explain what happened at home, and to talk about Maria's predicament on the mountain; but there isn't space for both things in a piece of this length. Neither narrative strand has room to develop convincingly.

The first-person viewpoint isn't consistent.

If the badgers are "**out of sight**" and "**silent**", how does Maria know about them? How is she able to tell us what her parents said and did while she vanished among the trees?

These things mess up the story's perspective. Are we looking from Maria's point of view, or from the viewpoint of an omniscient (all-knowing) narrator?

There's too much reliance on adjectives.

This story tries to paint the scene vividly, but it uses a limited range of tools to achieve this. Far too often, it stacks up adjectives in a distracting way.

Even in the first paragraph, we have "**grey, stony**", "**cold, unwelcoming**", "**cheerful**" and "**bouncy, needle-strewn**". When there are this many adjectives, readers are unlikely to properly absorb all of them. What's more, you might as well attach a big sticker reading "**This Is Descriptive Writing**" to your work: the effect is over-the-top and annoying.

On the other hand ...

There are good things too, of course. The parents' characters are brought out well, there's some fairly interesting dialogue, and details such as the moment when Maria cuts off her ponytail make good use of sensory imagery.

TIME FOR ANOTHER GO

You've already planned and written a story based on the picture. You've also had the opportunity to read and assess two example stories and compare them with your own work.

By now, you probably have a lot of ideas for improving your story, or writing a completely new one.

The following space is for you to have another go.

FOLLOW-UP TASK

If you'd like some more practice, you can have a go at the following task.

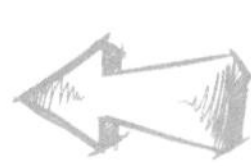

Somebody has arranged a meeting with you in this building.

When you arrive, you discover that the person waiting for you is not who you expected.

You must write in the past tense and in the first person: for example, "**I was …**".

Write between one and two pages.

RESOURCES
TO PRINT
AND KEEP

9:30—12:30

ZOOM

Teams

donnabutton2@Hotmail.
com.

9781916193185

BV - #0009 - 191120 - C93 - 297/210/5 - PB - 9781916193185